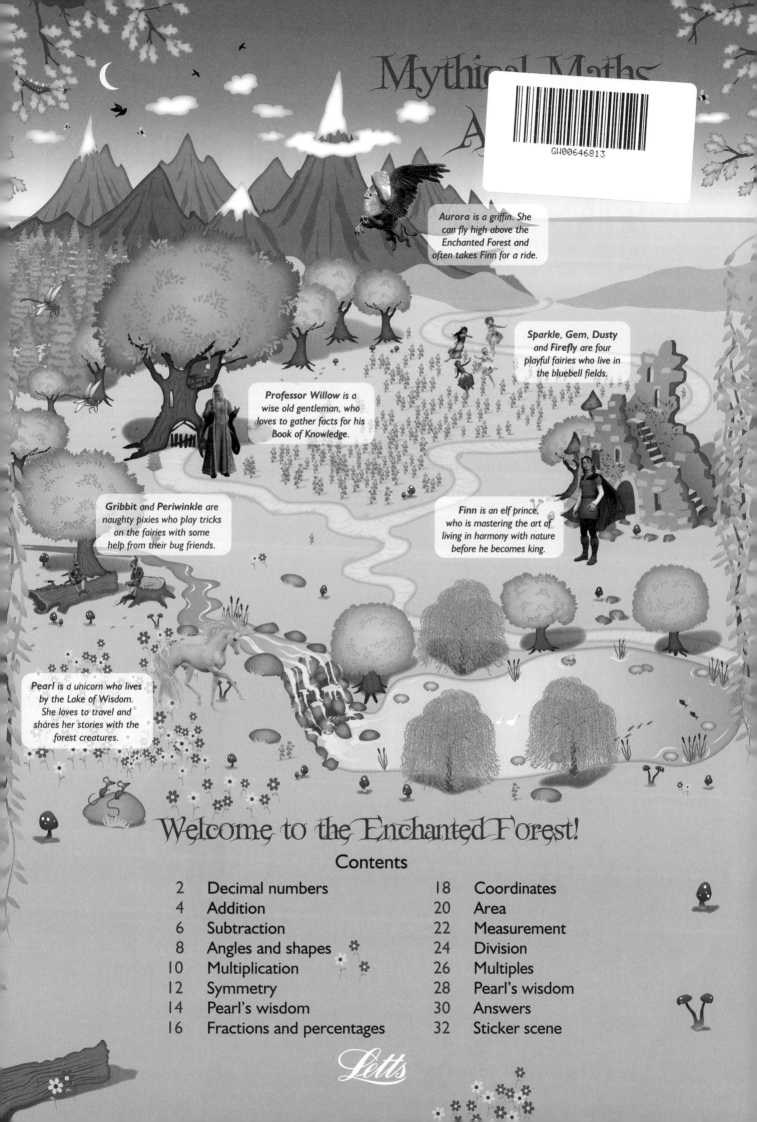

Mythical Maths

Aurora is a griffin. She can fly high above the Enchanted Forest and often takes Finn for a ride.

Sparkle, Gem, Dusty and Firefly are four playful fairies who live in the bluebell fields.

Professor Willow is a wise old gentleman, who loves to gather facts for his Book of Knowledge.

Gribbit and Periwinkle are naughty pixies who play tricks on the fairies with some help from their bug friends.

Finn is an elf prince, who is mastering the art of living in harmony with nature before he becomes king.

Pearl is a unicorn who lives by the Lake of Wisdom. She loves to travel and shares her stories with the forest creatures.

Welcome to the Enchanted Forest!

Contents

Letts

Decimal numbers

I'm Professor Willow. Shall we get straight to the point of this lesson?

Points are important. A decimal point separates whole numbers from decimal fractions.

27.84

2 tens (20)   7 ones (7)   8 tenths $\frac{8}{10}$ 4 hundredths $\frac{4}{100}$

This is read as twenty-seven point eight four.

Separate each decimal number into whole numbers and fractions. Write the missing numbers to complete these tables.

a

| 1 | 6 | . | 7 | 2 |

| 10 | ☐ | . | $\frac{☐}{10}$ | $\frac{☐}{100}$ |

b

| 3 | 8 | . | 1 | 5 |

| ☐ | 8 | . | $\frac{1}{☐}$ | $\frac{5}{☐}$ |

c

| 2 | 4 | . | 4 | 2 |

| ☐ | ☐ | . | $\frac{☐}{☐}$ | $\frac{☐}{☐}$ |

d

| 9 | 5 | . | 8 | 6 |

| 90 | ☐ | . | $\frac{☐}{10}$ | $\frac{☐}{100}$ |

 Rearrange this set of digits to make 6 different decimal numbers between 1 and 10. Use each digit only once in each decimal number.

4   6   5

a   __ . __ __   __ . __ __   __ . __ __   __ . __ __   __ . __ __   __ . __ __

b   Write the decimal numbers you have made in order, starting with the smallest.

__ . __ __   __ . __ __   __ . __ __   __ . __ __   __ . __ __   __ . __ __

 Write in the decimal number that each arrow points to.

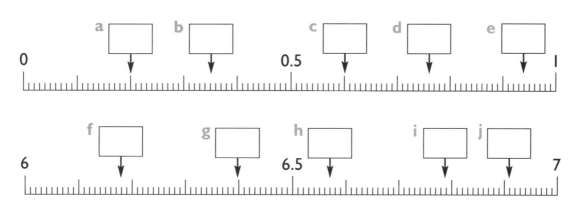

Willow's Quest

Now circle the correct answer for each of these.

a   What is $9\frac{7}{100}$ as a decimal?   9.7   9.700   9.07

b   What is 5.09 as a fraction? $5\frac{9}{10}$ $5\frac{9}{100}$ $5\frac{90}{100}$

c   What number is the arrow pointing to?

4.5   4.25   4.15

4   ↓   4.2

d   What number is the arrow pointing to?

8.59   8.61   8.6

8.5   ↓   8.7

Place this sticker of the treasure chest on the map at the back of this book.

Addition

We're Gribbit and Periwinkle. We'll show you how to add faster than the fairies!

What is 3492 added to 2631?

Step 1: Add the units.

```
  3 4 9 2    2 + 1 = 3
+ 2 6 3 1
──────────
        3
```

Step 2: Add the tens.

```
  3 4 9 2    90 + 30 = 120
+ 2 6 3 1
──────────
      2 3
      ₁
```

Step 3: Add the hundreds.

```
  3 4 9 2    100 + 400 + 600 = 1100
+ 2 6 3 1
──────────
    1 2 3
    ₁ ₁
```

Step 4: Add the thousands.

```
  3 4 9 2    1000 + 3000 + 2000 = 6000
+ 2 6 3 1
──────────
  6 1 2 3
    ₁ ₁
```

When you add numbers using a written method, make sure that you line up the columns carefully.

1 **Use this method to answer these sums.**

a
```
  6 7 2 8
+ 2 7 4 0
──────────
  8 1 6 8
```

b
```
  3 1 2 8
+ 4 6 7 5
──────────
  7 7 9 1
```

c
```
  1 5 6 1
+ 2 9 1 8
──────────
  3 1 7 9
```

d
```
  4 8 7 0
+ 4 6 9 3
──────────
        1 3
```

e
```
  3 6 6 7
+ 3 8 4 3
──────────
  6 1 1 1
```

f
```
  2 0 3 5
+ 1 9 8 5
──────────
  3 9 1 1
```

② Bring on the bugs! We've boxed some bugs and written how many are in each box. Work out the different totals when two boxes are put together.

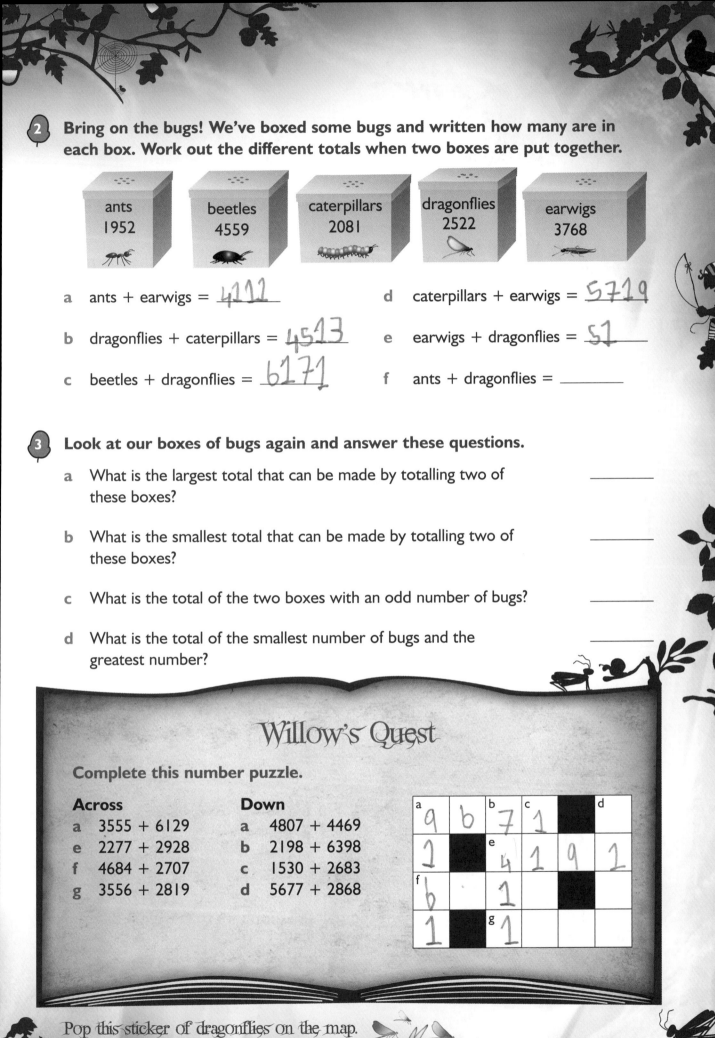

ants 1952   beetles 4559   caterpillars 2081   dragonflies 2522   earwigs 3768

a   ants + earwigs = _4112_

b   dragonflies + caterpillars = _4513_

c   beetles + dragonflies = _6171_

d   caterpillars + earwigs = _5719_

e   earwigs + dragonflies = _51_

f   ants + dragonflies = _____

③ Look at our boxes of bugs again and answer these questions.

a   What is the largest total that can be made by totalling two of these boxes?   _____

b   What is the smallest total that can be made by totalling two of these boxes?   _____

c   What is the total of the two boxes with an odd number of bugs?   _____

d   What is the total of the smallest number of bugs and the greatest number?   _____

Willow's Quest

Complete this number puzzle.

Across
a   3555 + 6129
e   2277 + 2928
f   4684 + 2707
g   3556 + 2819

Down
a   4807 + 4469
b   2198 + 6398
c   1530 + 2683
d   5677 + 2868

a 9	6	b 7	c 1		d
2		e 4	1	9	2
f 6		1			
1		g 1			

Pop this sticker of dragonflies on the map.

5

Subtraction

I'm Pearl and I know many interesting ways to subtract.

Follow these steps carefully and let's do this subtraction together.

$$3674 - 1738 = ?$$

Step 1: Subtract the units.

Rename 70 + 4 as 60 + 14

$$\begin{array}{r} 3\ 6\ {}^6\!7\ {}^1\!4 \\ -\ 1\ 7\ 3\ 8 \\ \hline 6 \end{array}$$ $14 - 8 = 6$

Step 2: Subtract the tens.

$$\begin{array}{r} 3\ 6\ {}^6\!7\ {}^1\!4 \\ -\ 1\ 7\ 3\ 8 \\ \hline 3\ 6 \end{array}$$ $60 - 30 = 30$

Step 3: Subtract the hundreds.

Rename 3000 + 600 as 2000 + 1600

$$\begin{array}{r} {}^2\!3\ {}^1\!6\ {}^6\!7\ {}^1\!4 \\ -\ 1\ 7\ 3\ 8 \\ \hline 9\ 3\ 6 \end{array}$$ $1600 - 700 = 900$

Step 4: Subtract the thousands.

Rename 3000 + 600 as 2000 + 1600

$$\begin{array}{r} {}^2\!3\ {}^1\!6\ {}^6\!7\ {}^1\!4 \\ -\ 1\ 7\ 3\ 8 \\ \hline 1\ 9\ 3\ 6 \end{array}$$ $2000 - 1000 = 1000$

1 Complete these subtractions. Take your time.

a
$$\begin{array}{r} 7\ 8\ 4\ 6 \\ -\ 6\ 6\ 1\ 2 \\ \hline \end{array}$$

b
$$\begin{array}{r} 8\ 3\ 9\ 1 \\ -\ 7\ 1\ 5\ 7 \\ \hline \end{array}$$

c
$$\begin{array}{r} 3\ 0\ 7\ 2 \\ -\ 1\ 8\ 3\ 8 \\ \hline \end{array}$$

d
$$\begin{array}{r} 4\ 2\ 1\ 1 \\ -\ 2\ 9\ 7\ 7 \\ \hline \end{array}$$

e
$$\begin{array}{r} 5\ 1\ 0\ 6 \\ -\ 3\ 8\ 7\ 2 \\ \hline \end{array}$$

f
$$\begin{array}{r} 6\ 3\ 2\ 8 \\ -\ 5\ 0\ 9\ 4 \\ \hline \end{array}$$

2 Use the magic within you to join the pairs of numbers that have a difference of 1299.

1083   2495   3299   2382

1848   2000   3147   1196

3 This table shows the depths of the deepest oceans and seas in the world. Look at the table and answer these questions.

Ocean/sea	Average depth (metres)
Pacific Ocean	4028m
Indian Ocean	3963m
Atlantic Ocean	3926m
Caribbean Sea	2647m
South China Sea	1652m
Bering Sea	1547m
Gulf of Mexico	1486m
Mediterranean Sea	1429m

a How much deeper is the Caribbean Sea than the Gulf of Mexico? _____

b By how many metres is the Pacific Ocean deeper than the Caribbean Sea? _____

c What is the difference in depth between the Atlantic Ocean and the Caribbean Sea? _____

d Which two seas have a difference in depth of 1100m? _____

e Which sea is 1316m less in depth than the Indian Ocean? _____

Willow's Quest

Write the missing digits in these subtractions.

a
```
    3  8  4  ☐
 -  1  7  ☐  2
 ───────────
    2  ☐  8  5
```

b
```
    7  ☐  4  3
 -  2  4  8  ☐
 ───────────
    ☐  4  5  7
```

c
```
    4  1  1  5
 -  2  ☐  3  ☐
 ───────────
    ☐  1  7  9
```

Put the frog sticker on the map.

Angles and shapes

I'm Finn. Let's search for the truth behind these angles.

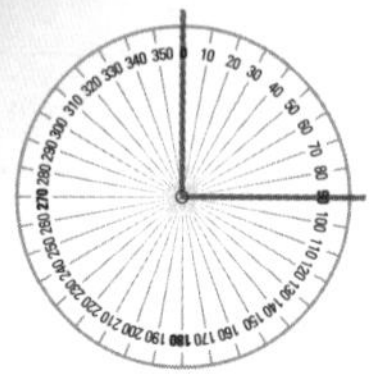

90° is a right angle.

Acute angles **are** less than 90°.

Obtuse angles **are** between 90° and 180°.

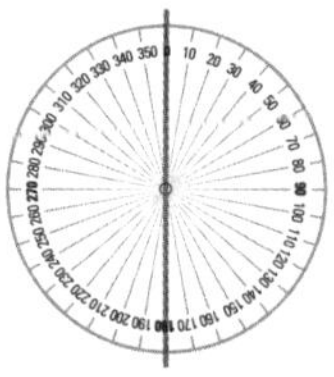

A straight line **is** 180°.

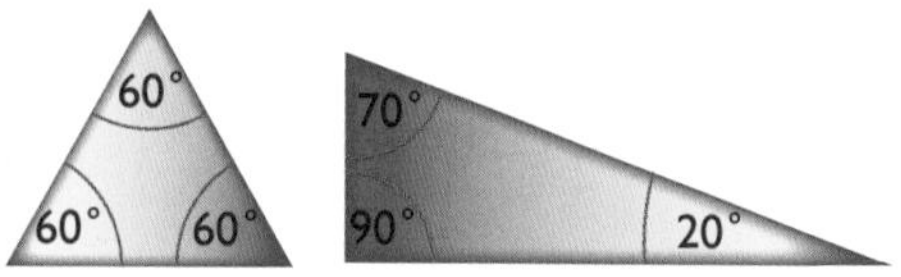

60°
60° 60°

70°
90° 20°

90° 90°
90° 90°

130°
50° 50°
130°

All the angles of a triangle total 180°.

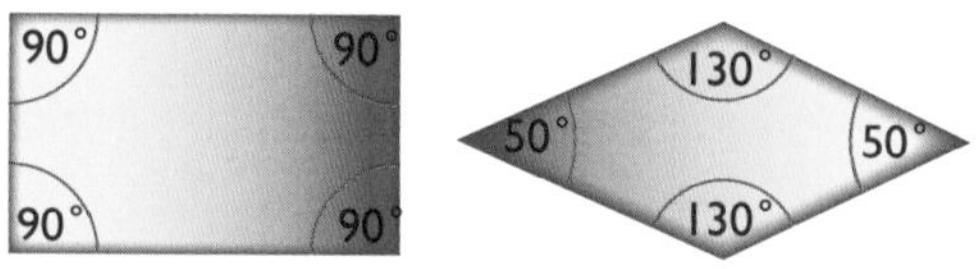

All the angles of a quadrilateral total 360°.

Angles are measured in degrees (°).

Once you have mastered estimating the size of each angle, try measuring each angle using a protractor. Write your results and complete this table.

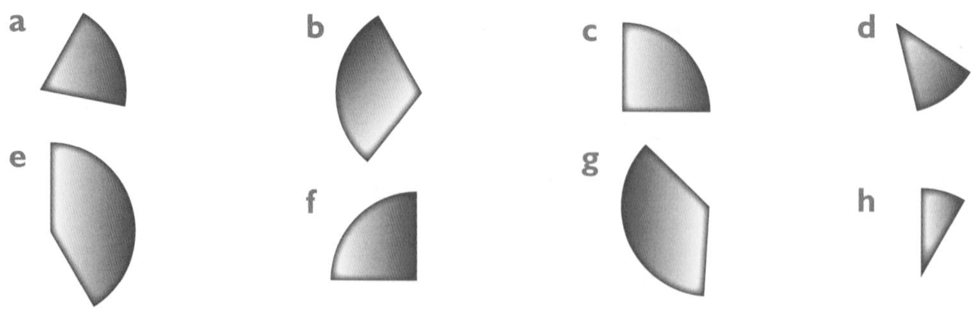

a

b

c

d

e

f

g

h

Angle	a	b	c	d	e	f	g	h
Estimated size (°)								
Measured size (°)								

2 Now try these, number warrior. Write letters in each corner of these shapes to show whether the angles are:

a acute   o obtuse   r right-angled

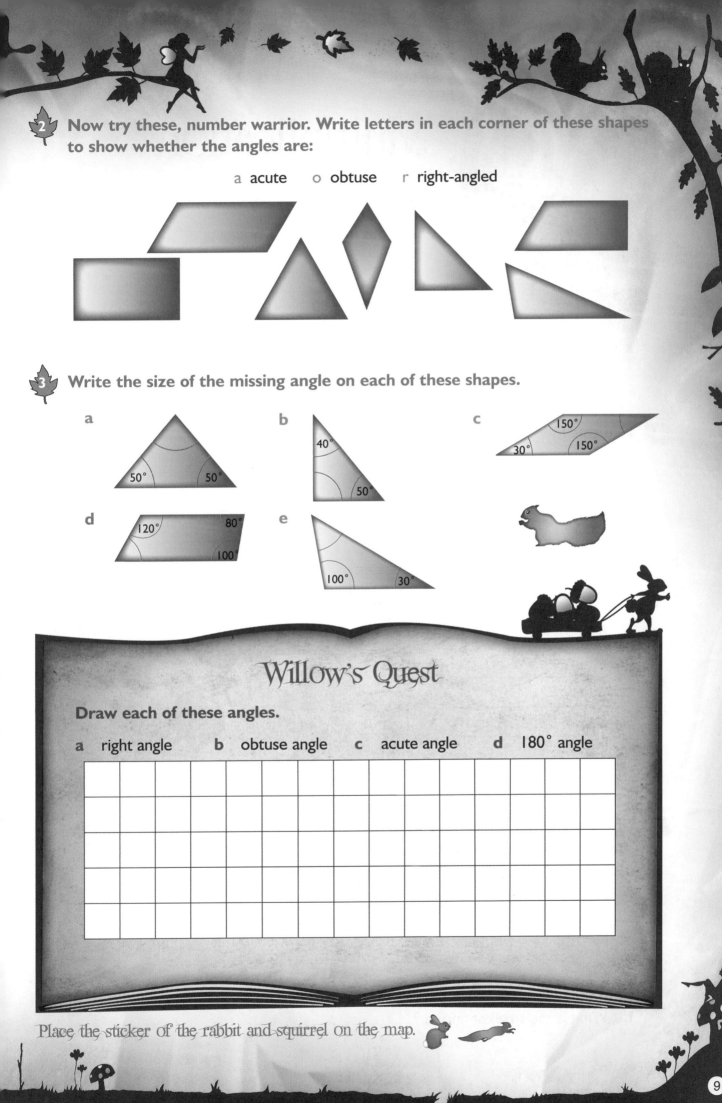

3 Write the size of the missing angle on each of these shapes.

a

b

c
150°
30°   150°

40°
50°

50°   50°

d
120°   80°
100°

e
100°   30°

Willow's Quest

Draw each of these angles.

a right angle   b obtuse angle   c acute angle   d 180° angle

Place the sticker of the rabbit and squirrel on the map.

Multiplication

My name is Aurora. Fly with me and learn to multiply.

Look at this method for working out 34 x 26:

x	30	4	
20	600	80	680
6	180	24	+ 204
			884

1 Use this method to complete these multiplications.

a 19 x 76 = _____

x	10	9
70		
6		

+ ▭
▭

c 62 x 43 = _____

x	60	2
40		
3		

+ ▭
▭

b 84 x 37 = _____

x	80	4
30		
7		

+ ▭
▭

2 I have collected the digits 3, 4, 5 and 6 in my nest. Arrange these digits to make different multiplications.

▭▭ × ▭▭   ▭▭ × ▭▭

a What is the largest answer you can make? _____

b What is the smallest answer? _____

3 Read and answer these multiplication problems.

a   There are 24 hours in a day. How many hours are there in June?   _____

b   Aurora flies 56km to take Professor Willow to the Glade of
Yesterday and back. She takes him 18 times in October. How far
did they travel in total in October?   _____

c   One of Periwinkle's arrows weighs 28g and a full quiver holds
45 arrows. How many grams do the arrows weigh altogether
in a full quiver?   _____

d   At the Enchanted Ball there were 32 cakes, each weighing 75g.
What was the total weight of cake mixture in this recipe?   _____

e   There are 15 balloons in a pack and Gribbit orders 47 packs for
the Enchanted Ball. How many balloons will there be altogether?   _____

f   What is 34 multiplied by 27?   _____

g   What is 16 times 23?   _____

h   Multiply 81 by 19.   _____

i   What is the product of 33 and 52?   _____

j   What number is 40 times greater than 29?   _____

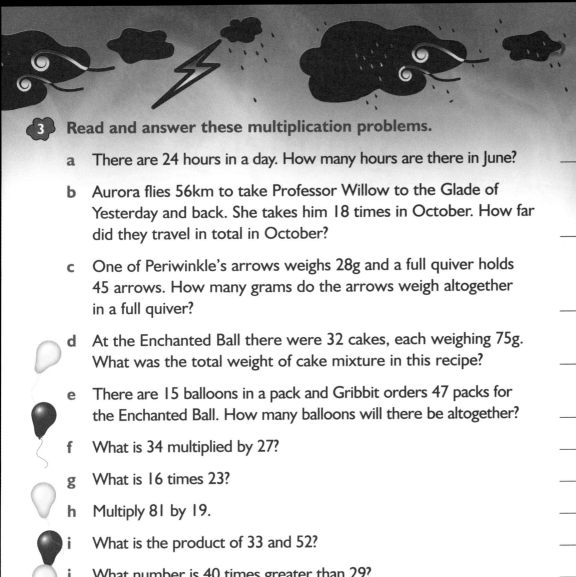

Willow's Quest

Circle the missing number in each of these.

a   70 x ? = 2100   3   30   300

b   15 x 16 = ?   240   380   180

c   ? x 42 = 1680   44   45   40

d   38 x 26 = ?   648   988   1048

Place the sticker of the birds on the map. You're a star!

Symmetry

We're Gem and Sparkle.

A line of symmetry divides a shape in half. One half is the reflection of the other half.

The line of symmetry is the same as a mirror line.

Some shapes have no lines of symmetry, but others have one or more.

I Draw lines of symmetry on these shapes.

a

b

c

d

e

f

2 Let's tidy up these quadrilaterals and put them into two groups, symmetrical or not symmetrical. Join each shape to the correct box.

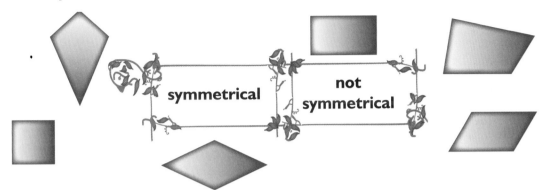

symmetrical

not symmetrical

3 Colour these pentagons to make three different symmetrical designs.

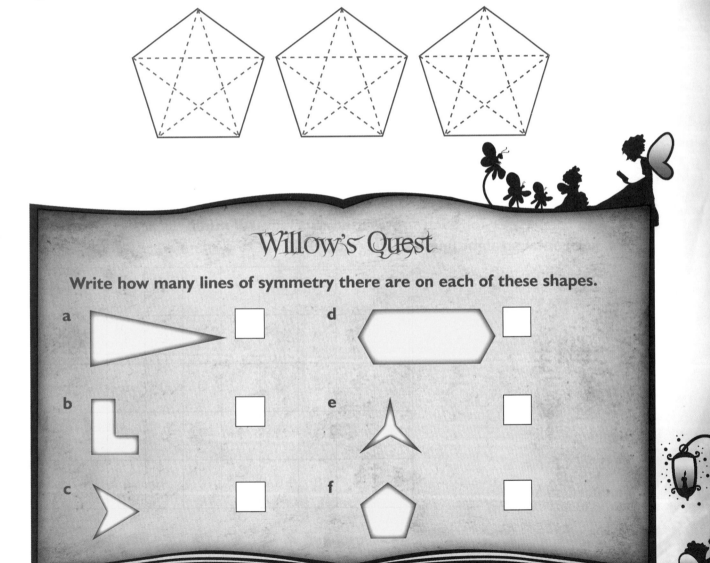

Willow's Quest

Write how many lines of symmetry there are on each of these shapes.

a ☐   d ☐

b ☐   e ☐

c ☐   f ☐

Place the sticker of bluebells on the map.

Pearl's wisdom

1 Use the magic within you to write these as decimals.

a 7 tenths _____

b 9 tenths _____

c 3 tenths _____

d 6 tenths _____

e 26 hundredths _____

f 35 hundredths _____

g 12 hundredths _____

h 78 hundredths _____

2 The digits 4 and 5 are missing from these additions. Complete the additions with the digits in the correct place.

```
   3 ☐ 8 1
 + ☐ 6 9 ☐
   9 1 7 ☐
```

```
   ☐ 3 6 8
 + 1 ☐ 9 ☐
   ☐ 8 6 3
```

```
   1 ☐ 6 8
 + ☐ 2 ☐ 7
   6 8 2 ☐
```

3 Circle the answer for each subtraction carefully. All numbers are in a vertical or horizontal straight line, not diagonally.

9558 – 5696 = _3862_

7487 – 3513 = _3974_

6094 – 1906 = _____

9250 – 5937 = _____

8449 – 2939 = _____

4076 – 2781 = _____

3558 – 1391 = _____

8000 – 1276 = _____

7487 – 2423 = _____

9200 – 4760 = _____

3	8	6	2	3	6	1	2	9	5
9	9	9	2	3	6	0	1	8	0
7	7	5	5	1	0	0	6	7	6
4	1	1	3	3	9	6	7	2	4
4	1	8	8	6	4	4	4	0	5

4 Look at these angles and complete this chart. Tick to show whether each angle is acute, obtuse or right-angled. Measure each angle and write the size on the chart.

a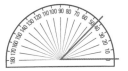

b

c

d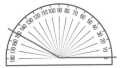

e

f

Angle	a	b	c	d	e	f
Acute						
Obtuse						
Right-angled						
Measured size (°)						

5 This is an order form for equipment for Professor Willow's maths lesson with the local pixies. Write how many of each item has been ordered.

Items	Amount in 1 pack	Number of packs	Total number of items
Pencils	28	76	
Chalk	15	33	
Sharpeners	26	19	
Pens	52	58	

6 Circle the correct answers to the questions below.

a Which quadrilateral is symmetrical?

b How many lines of symmetry does this shape have? 6 2 3

Place the crystals sticker on the map.

Fractions and percentages

Percentages are hundredths. The percentage sign is %.

$$30\% = \frac{30}{100}$$

Common percentages are:

$$10\% = \frac{10}{100} = \frac{1}{10} \qquad 25\% = \frac{25}{100} = \frac{1}{4}$$

$$20\% = \frac{20}{100} = \frac{1}{5} \qquad 75\% = \frac{75}{100} = \frac{3}{4}$$

To change fractions to percentages, **make them** out of 100:

$$\frac{7}{10} = \frac{70}{100} = 70\% \qquad \frac{4}{5} = \frac{80}{100} = 80\%$$

1 Draw a line to join each fraction to the matching percentage.

52% 14% $\frac{1}{4}$ 50%

 $\frac{45}{100}$ $\frac{15}{100}$ $\frac{40}{100}$ 15%

 $\frac{1}{5}$ 45%   20%   25%

 $\frac{14}{100}$ $\frac{52}{100}$ $\frac{1}{2}$ 40%

Enchanted Forest Map Stickers

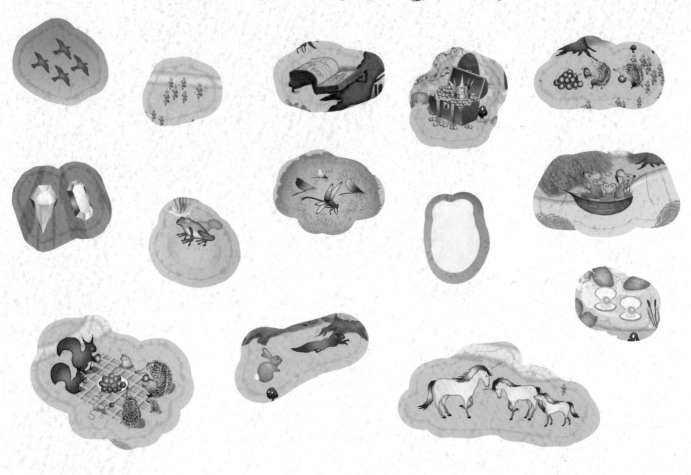

Extra Stickers

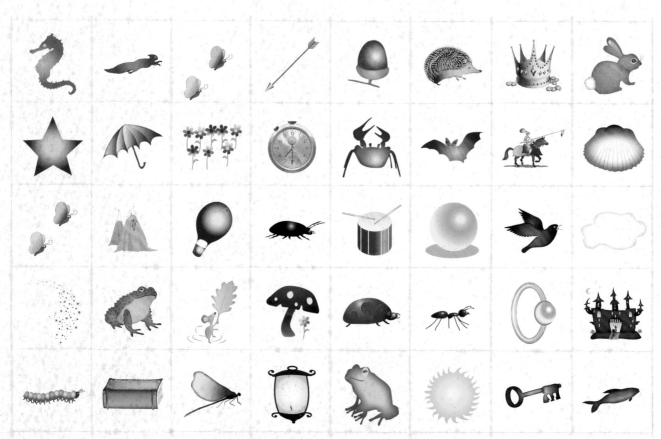

Forest
Friends

2 Write these percentages as fractions. Then write the fractions in their simplest form. For example, $10\% = \frac{10}{100} = \frac{1}{10}$.

a 20% = $\frac{\quad}{\quad}$ = $\frac{\quad}{\quad}$

d 80% = $\frac{\quad}{\quad}$ = $\frac{\quad}{\quad}$

b 75% = $\frac{\quad}{\quad}$ = $\frac{\quad}{\quad}$

e 25% = $\frac{\quad}{\quad}$ = $\frac{\quad}{\quad}$

c 50% = $\frac{\quad}{\quad}$ = $\frac{\quad}{\quad}$

3 Colour this grid with your pencils to match the percentages for each colour.

Colour 50% yellow   Colour 5% brown

Colour 10% red   Colour 25% blue

Colour 10% green

Willow's Quest

These are the marks that Periwinkle scored in some maths tests.
Each test had a different number of questions and I want to compare
his scores. Change them all to percentages to work out which test this
student scored highest in and which he scored lowest in.

Test	Score	Percentage
1	$\frac{7}{10}$	
2	$\frac{18}{20}$	
3	$\frac{4}{5}$	
4	$\frac{21}{25}$	
5	$\frac{38}{50}$	

Highest score:

_____

Lowest score:

_____

Wonderful work! Place the sticker of mice fishing on the map.

Coordinates

The sky is the limit with coordinates. They help us to find a position on a grid.

Read along the horizontal axis first, then read up the vertical axis.

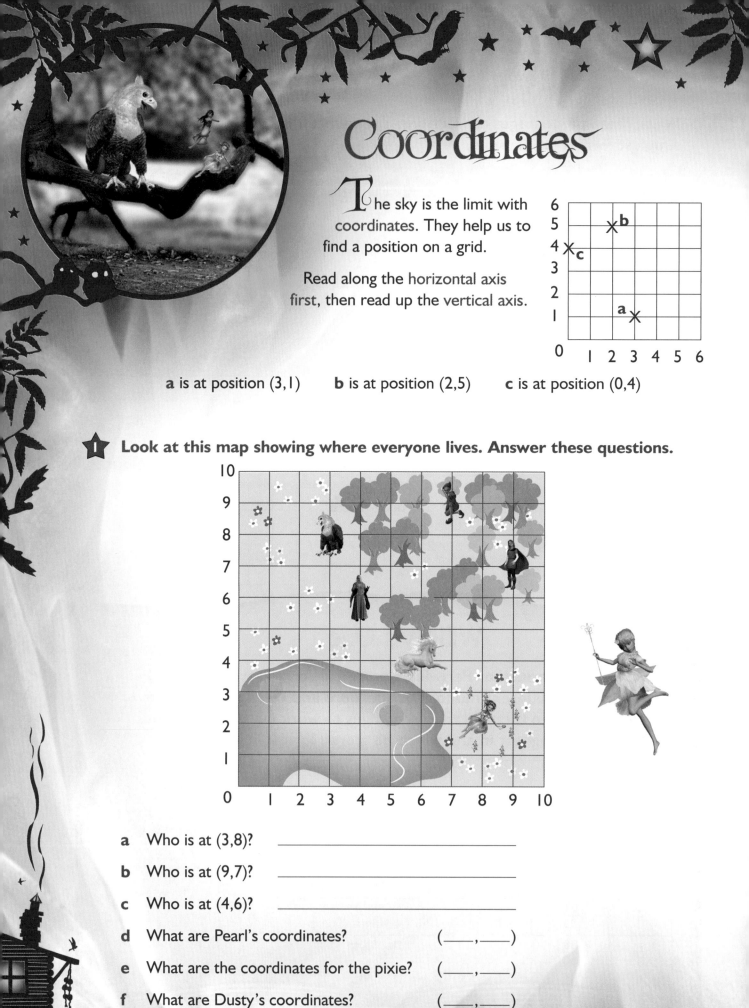

a is at position (3,1)   **b** is at position (2,5)   **c** is at position (0,4)

1 **Look at this map showing where everyone lives. Answer these questions.**

a Who is at (3,8)? _____

b Who is at (9,7)? _____

c Who is at (4,6)? _____

d What are Pearl's coordinates?   (___,___)

e What are the coordinates for the pixie?   (___,___)

f What are Dusty's coordinates?   (___,___)

2 **Now try this. Here are two sides of a square.**

a What are the coordinates of the three corners shown?

(—,—)   (—,—)   (—,—)

b Draw a cross for the missing coordinates for the fourth corner and complete the square.

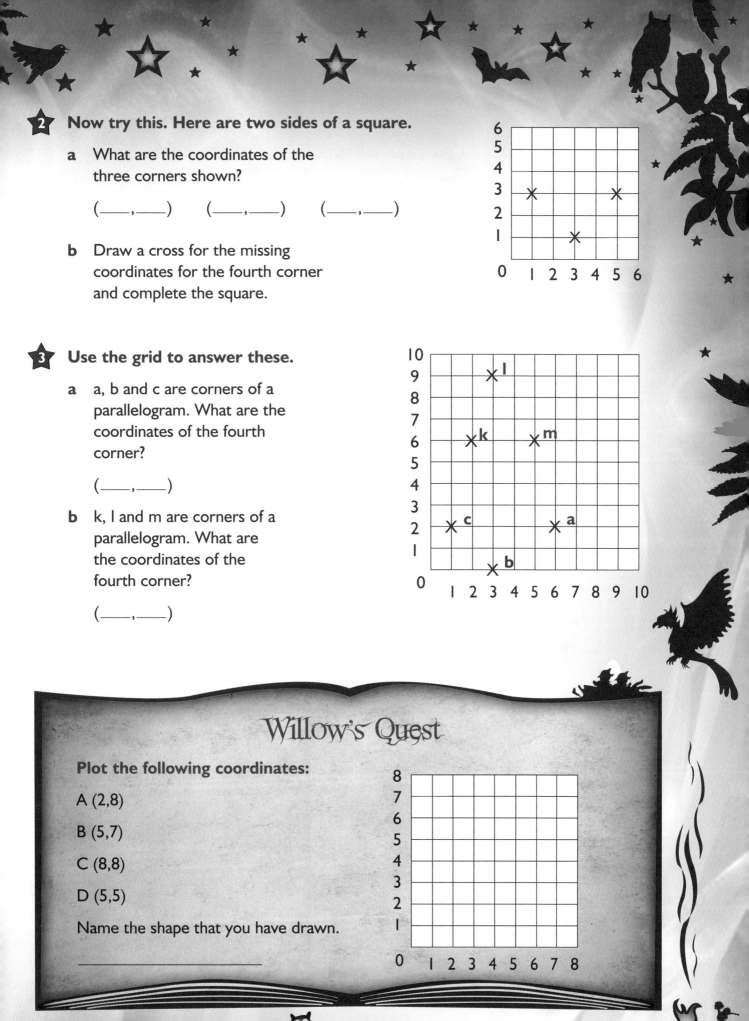

3 **Use the grid to answer these.**

a a, b and c are corners of a parallelogram. What are the coordinates of the fourth corner?

(—,—)

b k, l and m are corners of a parallelogram. What are the coordinates of the fourth corner?

(—,—)

Willow's Quest

Plot the following coordinates:

A (2,8)

B (5,7)

C (8,8)

D (5,5)

Name the shape that you have drawn.

_____

Place the owl sticker on the map.

19

Area

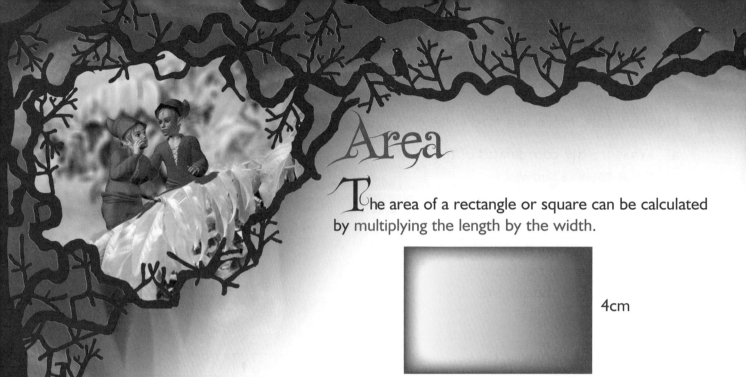

The area of a rectangle or square can be calculated by multiplying the length by the width.

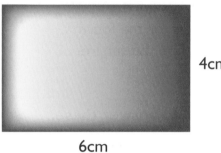

4cm

6cm

length x width = area

6cm x 4cm = 24cm^2

Area is measured in square units, such as square centimetres (cm^2) and square metres (m^2).

1 Lets get busy! Calculate the area of each of these shapes.

a
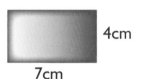
4cm

7cm

Area = _____ cm^2

b

5cm

5cm

Area = _____ cm^2

c
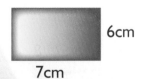
6cm

7cm

Area = _____ cm^2

d

8cm

10cm

Area = _____ cm^2

e

9cm

9cm

Area = _____ cm^2

f

3cm

11cm

Area = _____ cm^2

2 Use a ruler to measure the sides of these shapes in centimetres. Once you've measured the sides, try writing the area for each shape. Bugalicious!

a

area = _____ cm^2

c

area = _____ cm^2

b

area = _____ cm^2

d

area = _____ cm^2

Willow's Quest

These shapes are made from rectangles joined together. Write the total area of each shape. Colour the rectangles within the shape first to help you.

a

2cm
6cm
2cm   2cm
4cm

area = _____ cm^2

b

8cm   6cm
3cm
2cm

area = _____ cm^2

c

4cm
5cm
7cm
3cm
4cm
3cm   2cm

area = _____ cm^2

Place the sticker of hedgehogs on the map.

Measurement

Read this information about measurement carefully.

Measuring weight or mass

Weight and mass are closely linked but are not quite the same thing.

Metric units of mass are kilograms (kg) and grams (g).

1000 grams = 1 kilogram

2400g = 2.4kg

Measuring capacity

Capacity is about how much something holds.

Metric units of capacity are litres (l) and millilitres (ml).

1000 millilitres = 1 litre

1800ml = 1.8 l

'Weight' is often used to mean the same as 'mass'.

Mass is the amount of matter in an object.

Weight is the measurement of the force of gravity on an object.

1 Read these scales and write each weight in grams and kilograms.

a

 _____ g = _____ kg

d

 _____ g = _____ kg

b

 _____ g = _____ kg

e

 _____ g = _____ kg

c

 _____ g = _____ kg

f

 _____ g = _____ kg

2 Write the amount of water in each jug as millilitres and litres.

a _____ ml = _____ litres

d _____ ml = _____ litres

b _____ ml = _____ litres

e _____ ml = _____ litres

c _____ ml = _____ litres

f _____ ml = _____ litres

 3 Use the magic within you to draw water in each jug to match the measurement.

a

I litre

b

800ml

c

200ml

Willow's Quest

Write each set of measures in order, starting with the smallest.

a   800ml   330ml   0.5 litres   3.3 litres   5000ml   8 litres

_____ _____ _____ _____ _____ _____

b   1.4kg   4100g   440g   0.4kg   4kg   40g

_____ _____ _____ _____ _____ _____

Take your time and place the sticker of the unicorns  on the map.

Division

If a number cannot be divided exactly, it leaves a remainder.

What is 749 divided by 4?

Work out how many groups of 4 there are in 749 and what is left over:

Method 1

```
      1 8 7 r 1
  4 | 7 4 9
  -   4 0 0        (4 x 100)
      3 4 9
  -   3 2 0        (4 x 80)
        2 9
  -     2 8        (4 x 7)
          1
```

Method 2

```
        1 8 7 r 1
  4 | 7 ³4 ²9
```

 Divide these and write the answer with a remainder. Bugalicious!

Use method 1:

a
```
4 | 5 2 9
```

b
```
8 | 4 1 2
```

c
```
5 | 3 8 6
```

Use method 2:

d
```
9 | 3 8 0
```

e
```
3 | 2 4 5
```

f
```
3 | 7 9 0
```

2 Try these pongy problems. Read the questions and fill in the answers.

a   There are 366 days in a leap year. How many full weeks are there and how many days are left over? _____ weeks and _____ days

b   How many 5 cm lengths can be cut from 133 cm of string? _____ lengths

How much string is left over? _____ cm

c   138 flowers are divided into bunches of nine flowers

How many bunches of flowers can be made? _____ bunches

How many flowers are left over? _____ flowers

3 We keep the forest tidy after annoying humans have visited and left a mess. The rubbish we collect each day is put into bags, with exactly 6 items in each bag. Write down how many bags are completely filled each day and how many bits of rubbish are left over.

Day of the week	Bits of rubbish collected	Number of full bags (6 items)	Bits of rubbish left over
Monday	627		
Tuesday	572		
Wednesday	700		
Thursday	644		
Friday	683		

Willow's Quest

Find the remainder for each of these and then circle the number in this word search.

a   359 ÷ 10   f   506 ÷ 4

b   856 ÷ 3   g   478 ÷ 5

c   764 ÷ 9   h   515 ÷ 6

d   123 ÷ 7   i   542 ÷ 8

e   223 ÷ 9

T	S	I	X	A	T
H	E	V	I	F	H
G	V	T	W	O	R
I	E	N	O	U	E
E	N	I	N	R	E

Place the sticker of the woodland picnic on the map.

Multiples

Multiples are amazing. A multiple of a whole number is produced by multiplying that number by another whole number.

Multiples of 3:		3	6	9	**12**	15	18...	60...	300...
Multiples of 4:		4	8	**12**	16	20	24...	80...	400...

12 is a multiple of both 3 and 4.

This means that 12 is a common multiple of 3 and 4.

Colour multiples to find the routes for Periwinkle and Gribbit to get across this maze. They can move up, down or sideways, but not diagonally.

Colour multiples of 6 orange to show Periwinkle's path across the maze.

Colour multiples of 8 yellow to show Gribbit's path across the maze.

START →

6	54	44	19	18	42	36	38	44	64	24	→ FINISH
9	60	26	64	48	8	30	50	40	56	65	
14	36	12	24	30	56	54	12	80	81	21	
28	35	16	80	45	16	64	48	32	52	25	

START →

8	32	40	20	49	14	63	42	18	54	24	→ FINISH

2 Write the first 10 multiples for each of these. No time like the present!

a multiples of 4

b multiples of 3

c multiples of 6

d multiples of 5

e multiples of 10

f multiples of 8

3 Look at your answers for question 2. Use the lists of multiples to help you find the common multiples for each of these pairs of numbers.

a 3 and 5

b 4 and 3

c 4 and 5

d 6 and 8

e 10 and 6

f 6 and 4

Willow's Quest

Use these numbers to answer each question.

12   15   27   32

a Which number is a multiple of 5?

b Which two numbers are multiples of 4?

c Which number is not a multiple of 3?

d Which number is a common multiple of 9 and 3?

e Which number is the lowest common multiple of 6 and 4?

Place the sticker of my Book of Knowledge on the map.

Pearl's wisdom

1 Use the magic within you to change each percentage into a fraction. Write the missing numbers to complete the fractions.

a 50%  $\dfrac{}{2}$

b 90% $\dfrac{}{10}$

c 60% $\dfrac{}{20}$

d 75% $\dfrac{}{4}$

e 30% $\dfrac{}{10}$

f 15% $\dfrac{}{20}$

2 Plot the following coordinates carefully:

A (2,8)
B (4,6)
C (4,4)
D (2,4)
E (0,6)

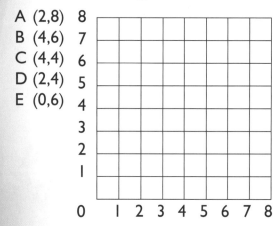

Join the coordinates with a ruler. What is the name of the shape you have drawn?

_____

3 Draw a line to match each division to a remainder.

 271 ÷ 6

359 ÷ 10

315 ÷ 8

 398 ÷ 7

 1   2   3   4   5   6   7 8 9

remainder

259 ÷ 9

454 ÷ 5

458 ÷ 9

608 ÷ 3

4 The Lake of Wisdom holds the answers! Use your pencils to colour in three sets of crabs with matching weights.

750g 2.25kg 0.75kg $2\frac{1}{4}$ kg 2250g

$\frac{3}{4}$ kg 1500g $1\frac{1}{2}$ kg 1.5kg

5 Take your time and measure the sides of each shape with a ruler. Write the area of each of these.

a

b

c

area = _____ cm^2 area = _____ cm^2 area = _____ cm^2

6 Write these numbers in the correct part of the Venn diagram.

12   4   18   10   24   16   15   3   20   9   6   25   8   30   36

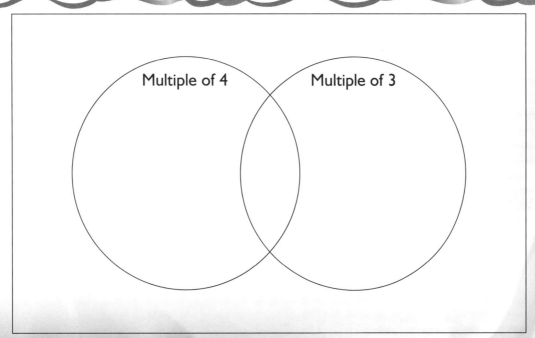

Multiple of 4   Multiple of 3

Complete the map with the pearls and shells sticker.

29

Answers

Pages 2–3

1. a 6, 7, 2
   b 30, 10, 100
   c 20, 4, $\frac{4}{10}$, $\frac{2}{100}$
   d 5, 8, 6
2. a decimals from b) in any order.
   b 4.56, 4.65, 5.46, 5.64, 6.45, 6.54
3. a 0.2
   b 0.35
   c 0.6
   d 0.76
   e 0.94
   f 6.18
   g 6.4
   h 6.57
   i 6.79
   j 6.91

Willow's Quest

a 9.07
b 5 $\frac{9}{100}$
c 4.15
d 8.59

Pages 4–5

1. a 9468
   b 7803
   c 4479
   d 9563
   e 7510
   f 4020
2. a 5720
   b 4603
   c 7081
   d 5849
   e 6290
   f 4474
3. a 8327
   b 4033
   c 6640
   d 6511

Willow's Quest

^{a}9	6	^{b}8	^{c}4		^{d}8
2		^{e}5	2	0	5
^{f}7	3	9	1		4
6		^{g}6	3	7	5

Pages 6–7

1. a 1234
   b 1234
   c 1234
   d 1234
   e 1234
   f 1234
2.

Pages 8–9

3. a 1161m
   b 1381m
   c 1279m
   d Caribbean and Bering Seas
   e Caribbean Sea

Willow's Quest

a
```
  3847
- 1762
  ----
  2085
```

b
```
  7943
- 2486
  ----
  5457
```

c
```
  4115
- 2936
  ----
  1179
```

Pages 8–9

1. The measured angles are:
   a 70°
   b 110°
   c 90°
   d 45°
   e 150°
   f 90°
   g 130°
   h 30°
2.
3. a 80°
   b 90°
   c 30°
   d 60°
   e 50°

Willow's Quest

Check that the angles have been drawn accurately.
Example angles are:

Pages 10–11

1. a 1444
   b 3108
   c 2666
2. a 3402
   b 1610
3. a 720
   b 1008km
   c 1260g
   d 2400g
   e 705
   f 918

g 368
h 1539
i 1716
j 1160

Willow's Quest

a 30
b 240
c 40
d 988

Pages 12–13

1. Check that the lines of symmetry are correct. There are other possible lines of symmetry for some shapes.

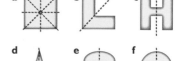

2.

3. Check that each design is symmetrical.

Willow's Quest

Pages 14–15

1. a 0.7
   b 0.9
   c 0.3
   d 0.6
   e 0.26
   f 0.35
   g 0.12
   h 0.78
2. a
```
  3481
+ 5694
  ----
  9175
```
   b
```
  4368
+ 1495
  ----
  5863
```
   c
```
  1568
+ 5257
  ----
  6825
```

3

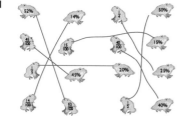

3	8	6	2	3	6	1	2	9	5
9	9	9	2	3	6	0	1	8	0
7	7	5	5	1	0	0	6	7	6
4	1	1	3	3	9	6	7	2	4
4	1	8	8	6	4	4	0	5

4

Angle	a	b	c	d	e	f
Acute	✓	✓				
Obtuse				✓	✓	
Right-angled			✓			✓
Measured size (°)	45	20	90	150	110	90

5
Pencils	2128
Chalk	495
Sharpeners	494
Pens	3016

6 a ◇ 
b 2

Pages 16–17
1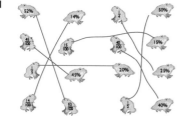

2 a $\frac{20}{100} = \frac{1}{5}$

b $\frac{75}{100} = \frac{3}{4}$

c $\frac{50}{100} = \frac{1}{2}$

d $\frac{80}{100} = \frac{4}{5}$

e $\frac{25}{100} = \frac{1}{4}$

3 Check that the squares coloured are as follows:
10 yellow
2 red
2 green
1 brown
5 blue

Willow's Quest
Test 1: 70%
Test 2: 90% .
Test 3: 80%
Test 4: 84%
Test 5: 76%
$\frac{7}{10}$ was the lowest score.
$\frac{18}{20}$ was the highest score.

Pages 18–19
1 a Aurora
b Finn
c Professor Willow
d (6,4)
e (7,9)
f (8,2)
2 a (1,3), (3,1), (5,3)
b

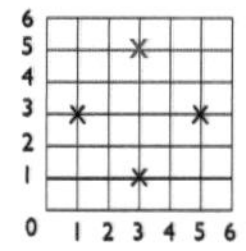

3 a (4,4)
b (6,9)

Willow's Quest
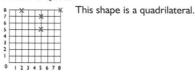 This shape is a quadrilateral.

Pages 20–21
1 a 28cm² **d** 80cm²
b 25cm² **e** 81cm²
c 42cm² **f** 33cm²
2 a 18cm²
b 10cm²
c 16cm²
d 15cm²

Willow's Quest
a 36cm²
b 34cm²
c 56cm²

Pages 22–23
1 a 500g = 0.5kg **d** 1900g = 1.9kg
b 800g = 0.8kg **e** 1250g = 1.25kg
c 1400g = 1.4kg **f** 750g = 0.75kg
2 a 2000ml = 2 litres
b 200ml = 0.2 litres
c 600ml = 0.6 litres
d 1100ml = 1.1 litres
e 250ml = 0.25 litres
f 1750ml = 1.75 litres
3 a

Willow's Quest
a 330ml, 0.5 litres, 800ml, 3.3 litres, 5000ml, 8 litres
b 40g, 0.4kg, 440g, 1.4kg, 4kg, 4100g

Pages 24–25
1 a 132 r1 **d** 42 r2
b 51 r4 **e** 81 r2
c 77 r1 **f** 263 r1
2 a 52 weeks and 2 days
b 26 lengths, 3cm left over
c 15 bunches, 3 flowers left over
3

Day of the week	Bits of rubbish collected	Number of full bags (6 items)	Bits of rubbish left over
Monday	627	104	3
Tuesday	572	95	2
Wednesday	700	116	4
Thursday	644	107	2
Friday	683	113	5

Willow's Quest
a r9 **b** r1 **c** r8
d r4 **e** r7 **f** r2
g r3 **h** r5 **i** r6

T	S	I	X	A	T
H	E	V	I	F	H
G	V	T	W	O	R
I	E	N	O	U	E
E	N	I	N	R	E

Pages 26–27
1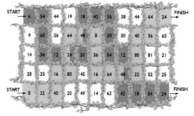

2 a 4, 8, 12, 16, 20, 24, 28, 32, 36, 40
b 3, 6, 9, 12, 15, 18, 21, 24, 27, 30
c 6, 12, 18, 24, 30, 36, 42, 48, 54, 60
d 5, 10, 15, 20, 25, 30, 35, 40, 45, 50
e 10, 20, 30, 40, 50, 60, 70, 80, 90, 100
f 8, 16, 24, 32, 40, 48, 56, 64, 72, 80
3 a 15, 30
b 12, 24
c 20, 40
d 24, 48
e 30, 60
f 12, 24, 36

Willow's Quest
a 15 **d** 27
b 12 and 32 **e** 12
c 32

Pages 28–29
1 a $\frac{1}{2}$

b $\frac{9}{10}$

c $\frac{12}{20}$

d $\frac{3}{4}$

e $\frac{3}{10}$

f $\frac{3}{20}$

2 Pentagon
3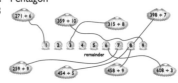

4 The three sets are:
$1\frac{1}{2}$kg, 1.5kg and 1500g
$\frac{3}{4}$kg, 0.75kg and 750g
$2\frac{1}{4}$kg, 2.25kg and 2250g
5 a 8cm²
b 9cm²
c 5cm²
6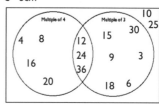